SNOOPY STARS

STARS

— AS —

THE TERROR OF THE ICE

Charles M. Schulz

RAVETTE BOOKS

This edition first published by
Ravette Books Limited 1988

Printed and bound in Great Britain
for Ravette Books Limited,
3 Glenside Estate, Star Road, Partridge Green,
Horsham, Sussex RH13 8RA
by Cox & Wyman Ltd, Reading

ISBN 1 85304 028 2

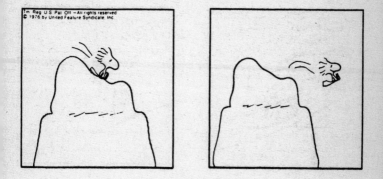

Tm Reg U S Pat Off – All rights reserved
© 1976 by United Feature Syndicate, Inc

© 1977 United Feature Syndicate, Inc.

11-22

DIDN'T SEE ANY POLAR BEARS, HUH?

THAT'S A GOOD IDEA.. TRY THE OTHER DIRECTION...

SNOOPY AND HIS LITTLE FRIEND WENT INTO THE WOODS TO CUT DOWN A CHRISTMAS TREE

THAT STUPID BEAGLE! DOESN'T HE KNOW YOU CAN'T JUST GO INTO THE WOODS, AND START CUTTING DOWN TREES?!

12-18

WHY NOT? WHO'S GOING TO CARE?

I NEVER REALIZED THAT SQUIRRELS COULD GET SO UPSET...

© 1980 United Feature Syndicate, Inc.

AS LONG AS WE'RE JUST PRACTICING, I HAVE A SUGGESTION

MAYBE YOU SHOULD SHOOT AT THE OTHER GOAL FOR A WHILE...

12-27

© 1983 United Feature Syndicate, Inc. 12-27

1-25 © 1983 United Feature Syndicate, Inc.

12-15

© 1984 United Feature Syndicate, Inc.

NEVER CATCH A FISH WHILE HE'S DOING AEROBICS...

THEY SAY IT MAY SNOW AGAIN TONIGHT

I JUST THOUGHT YOU MIGHT LIKE TO BE PREPARED...

Other Snoopy titles published by Ravette Books

Snoopy Stars in this series

No. 1 Snoopy Stars as The Flying Ace	£1.95
No. 2 Snoopy Stars as The Matchmaker	£1.95
No. 4 Snoopy Stars as The Legal Beagle	£1.95
No. 5 Snoopy Stars as The Fearless Leader	£1.95
No. 6 Snoopy Stars as Man's Best Friend	£1.95

Colour landscapes

First Serve	£2.95
Be Prepared	£2.95
Stay Cool	£2.95
Shall We Dance?	£2.95
Let's Go	£2.95
Come Fly With Me	£2.95

Black and white landscapes

It's a Dog's Life	£2.50
Roundup	£2.50
Freewheelin'	£2.50
Joe Cool	£2.50
Dogs Don't Eat Dessert	£2.50
You're on the Wrong Foot Again, Charlie Brown	£2.50

All these books are available at your local bookshop or news-agent, or can be ordered direct from the publisher. Just tick the titles you require and fill in the form below. Prices and availability subject to change without notice.

Ravette Books Limited, 3 Glenside Estate, Star Road, Partridge Green, Horsham, West Sussex RH13 8RA

Please send a cheque or postal order, and allow the following for postage and packing. UK: 45p for one book plus 30p for each additional book.

Name ....

Address ....

....